D1217056

Bob the Unorganized Zookeeper

Written and Illustrated by Duane Lightfoot III

LEMON HOUSE
PUBLISHING

© 2022 by Duane Lightfoot III
All rights reserved.

Lemon House Publishing, LLC
lemonhousepublishing.com

Lemon House Publishing strives to help young writers build confidence by guiding them through the process of writing and publishing their own children's books.

Designed by Lemon House Publishing

For my mom and my nana who help me stay organized and clean.

The zookeeper, Bob, is trying to feed the parrots but he does not know what parrots eat.

It's lunchtime and the parrots are hungry.

"We're hungry!" the parrots scream.

He looks in the car and finds some food, he puts it into the parrots bowl, but they don't eat it, it's the zebras' food.

So he looks in his car again but there isn't any more food in the car.

He looks in the parrot's cage and he thinks that he sees a bag, but it is just dirt.

He looks in the other animal cages like the monkeys' and the giraffes' cages, but nothing.

He walks all over the zoo. Then, goes up to the front of the zoo, but he doesn't find any bags of food there.

He takes a break to think about where he hasn't looked yet. Then he remembers the food storage room in the back of the zoo.

He runs over there. Past the lions, around the dolphins, and by the zebras, to get to the storage room.

He finds the food for the parrots and takes it to them and finally, feeds them nuts and fruits.

"Thank you!" the parrots say.

Bob decides that he should get more organized, and puts all the food on different shelves with different pictures of the animals.

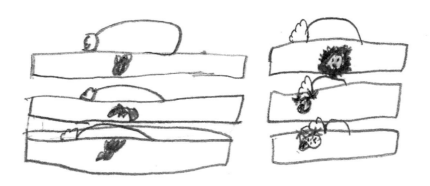

Made in the USA
Middletown, DE
03 June 2022

66624102R00015